Moontime Magic

Period Tracker

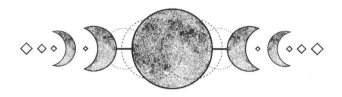

This book belongs to the amazing,
incredible and beautiful:

....

Using This Journal....

We are all unique and so are our cycles, and let's be honest, most of us dread the start of our "Moontime Magic". But using this journal will be your secret weapon to help you keep track of your period cycles and enable you to make more accurate predictions about how you will be feeling and when your next one will arrive.

The following pages are filled with prompts to get you thinking and noticing what happens to your body, mood and sleep during your cycle. So pour a cup of tea and open up that chocolate and complete as much or as little as you like.

♡ Jasmin Brooke xo

| J | F | M | A | M | J | J | A | S | O | N | D |

1	2	3	4	5	6	7	8	9	10	11	12
13	14	15	16	17	18	19	20	21	22	23	24
25	26	27	28	29	30	31	*Cross off dates that do not apply for this month				

KEY: ■ Heavy ◣ Medium △ Light • Spotting ⊠ N/A

_____ DAYS SINCE LAST PERIOD 🌙 EXPECT NEXT PERIOD AROUND_____

DAY ONE OF CYCLE

❑ Backaches ❑ Cramps   Sleep ☺ 😐 ☹
❑ Sore Breasts ❑ Acne   Energy ☺ 😐 ☹
❑ Cravings ❑ Other:_____ Mood ☺ 😐 ☹

_____

_____

_____

DAY TWO OF CYCLE

❑ Backaches ❑ Cramps   Sleep ☺ 😐 ☹
❑ Sore Breasts ❑ Acne   Energy ☺ 😐 ☹
❑ Cravings ❑ Other:_____ Mood ☺ 😐 ☹

_____

_____

_____

DAY THREE OF CYCLE

❑ Backaches ❑ Cramps   Sleep ☺ 😐 ☹
❑ Sore Breasts ❑ Acne   Energy ☺ 😐 ☹
❑ Cravings ❑ Other:_____ Mood ☺ 😐 ☹

_____

_____

_____

Year:_____

Day Four of Cycle

❏ Backaches ❏ Cramps   Sleep 🙂 😐 🙁
❏ Sore Breasts ❏ Acne   Energy 🙂 😐 🙁
❏ Cravings ❏ Other:_____   Mood 🙂 😐 🙁

_____

_____

_____

Day Five of Cycle

❏ Backaches ❏ Cramps   Sleep 🙂 😐 🙁
❏ Sore Breasts ❏ Acne   Energy 🙂 😐 🙁
❏ Cravings ❏ Other:_____   Mood 🙂 😐 🙁

_____

_____

_____

Day Six of Cycle

❏ Backaches ❏ Cramps   Sleep 🙂 😐 🙁
❏ Sore Breasts ❏ Acne   Energy 🙂 😐 🙁
❏ Cravings ❏ Other:_____   Mood 🙂 😐 🙁

_____

_____

_____

Day Seven of Cycle

❏ Backaches ❏ Cramps   Sleep 🙂 😐 🙁
❏ Sore Breasts ❏ Acne   Energy 🙂 😐 🙁
❏ Cravings ❏ Other:_____   Mood 🙂 😐 🙁

_____

_____

_____

| J | F | M | A | M | J | J | A | S | O | N | D |

1	2	3	4	5	6	7	8	9	10	11	12
13	14	15	16	17	18	19	20	21	22	23	24
25	26	27	28	29	30	31	*Cross off dates that do not apply for this month				

KEY: ■ Heavy ◣ Medium △ Light • Spotting ⊠ N/A

_____ DAYS SINCE LAST PERIOD ☾ EXPECT NEXT PERIOD AROUND_____

DAY ONE OF CYCLE

❏ Backaches   ❏ Cramps   Sleep ☺ 😐 ☹
❏ Sore Breasts ❏ Acne   Energy ☺ 😐 ☹
❏ Cravings   ❏ Other:_____ Mood ☺ 😐 ☹

_____

_____

DAY TWO OF CYCLE

❏ Backaches   ❏ Cramps   Sleep ☺ 😐 ☹
❏ Sore Breasts ❏ Acne   Energy ☺ 😐 ☹
❏ Cravings   ❏ Other:_____ Mood ☺ 😐 ☹

_____

_____

DAY THREE OF CYCLE

❏ Backaches   ❏ Cramps   Sleep ☺ 😐 ☹
❏ Sore Breasts ❏ Acne   Energy ☺ 😐 ☹
❏ Cravings   ❏ Other:_____ Mood ☺ 😐 ☹

_____

_____

Year:_____

Day Four of Cycle

- ❏ Backaches
- ❏ Sore Breasts
- ❏ Cravings
- ❏ Cramps
- ❏ Acne
- ❏ Other:_____

Sleep ☺ 😐 ☹
Energy ☺ 😐 ☹
Mood ☺ 😐 ☹

_____

_____

_____

Day Five of Cycle

- ❏ Backaches
- ❏ Sore Breasts
- ❏ Cravings
- ❏ Cramps
- ❏ Acne
- ❏ Other:_____

Sleep ☺ 😐 ☹
Energy ☺ 😐 ☹
Mood ☺ 😐 ☹

_____

_____

_____

Day Six of Cycle

- ❏ Backaches
- ❏ Sore Breasts
- ❏ Cravings
- ❏ Cramps
- ❏ Acne
- ❏ Other:_____

Sleep ☺ 😐 ☹
Energy ☺ 😐 ☹
Mood ☺ 😐 ☹

_____

_____

_____

Day Seven of Cycle

- ❏ Backaches
- ❏ Sore Breasts
- ❏ Cravings
- ❏ Cramps
- ❏ Acne
- ❏ Other:_____

Sleep ☺ 😐 ☹
Energy ☺ 😐 ☹
Mood ☺ 😐 ☹

_____

_____

_____

| J | F | M | A | M | J | J | A | S | O | N | D |

1	2	3	4	5	6	7	8	9	10	11	12
13	14	15	16	17	18	19	20	21	22	23	24
25	26	27	28	29	30	31	*Cross off dates that do not apply for this month				

KEY: ■ Heavy ◣ Medium △ Light • Spotting ⊠ N/A

_____ DAYS SINCE LAST PERIOD 🌙 EXPECT NEXT PERIOD AROUND_____

Day One of Cycle

❑ Backaches ❑ Cramps
❑ Sore Breasts ❑ Acne
❑ Cravings ❑ Other:_____

Sleep 🙂 😐 🙁
Energy 🙂 😐 🙁
Mood 🙂 😐 🙁

_____

_____

Day two of Cycle

❑ Backaches ❑ Cramps
❑ Sore Breasts ❑ Acne
❑ Cravings ❑ Other:_____

Sleep 🙂 😐 🙁
Energy 🙂 😐 🙁
Mood 🙂 😐 🙁

_____

_____

Day three of Cycle

❑ Backaches ❑ Cramps
❑ Sore Breasts ❑ Acne
❑ Cravings ❑ Other:_____

Sleep 🙂 😐 🙁
Energy 🙂 😐 🙁
Mood 🙂 😐 🙁

_____

_____

Day Four of Cycle

❏ Backaches ❏ Cramps   Sleep ☺ 😐 ☹
❏ Sore Breasts ❏ Acne   Energy ☺ 😐 ☹
❏ Cravings   ❏ Other:_____ Mood ☺ 😐 ☹

_____

_____

_____

Day Five of Cycle

❏ Backaches ❏ Cramps   Sleep ☺ 😐 ☹
❏ Sore Breasts ❏ Acne   Energy ☺ 😐 ☹
❏ Cravings   ❏ Other:_____ Mood ☺ 😐 ☹

_____

_____

_____

Day Six of Cycle

❏ Backaches ❏ Cramps   Sleep ☺ 😐 ☹
❏ Sore Breasts ❏ Acne   Energy ☺ 😐 ☹
❏ Cravings   ❏ Other:_____ Mood ☺ 😐 ☹

_____

_____

_____

Day Seven of Cycle

❏ Backaches ❏ Cramps   Sleep ☺ 😐 ☹
❏ Sore Breasts ❏ Acne   Energy ☺ 😐 ☹
❏ Cravings   ❏ Other:_____ Mood ☺ 😐 ☹

_____

_____

_____

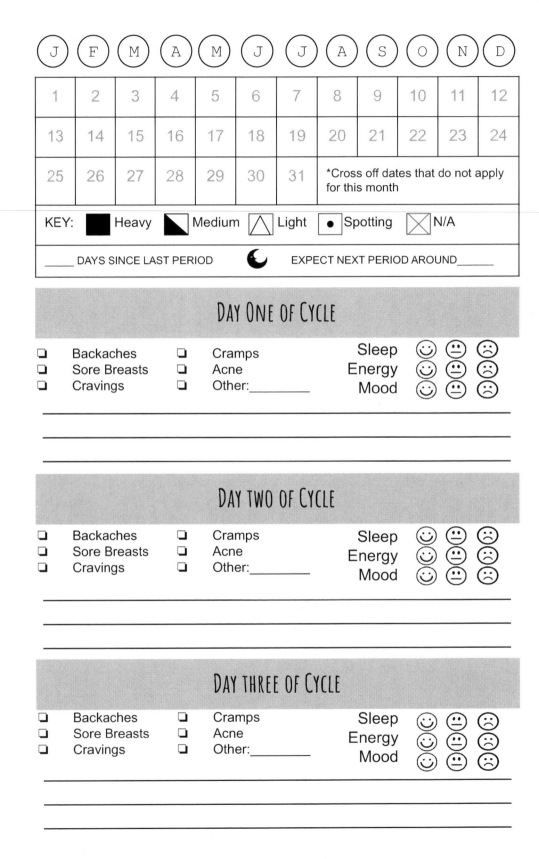

| J | F | M | A | M | J | J | A | S | O | N | D |

1	2	3	4	5	6	7	8	9	10	11	12
13	14	15	16	17	18	19	20	21	22	23	24
25	26	27	28	29	30	31	*Cross off dates that do not apply for this month				

KEY: ■ Heavy   ◨ Medium   △ Light   • Spotting   ⊠ N/A

_____ DAYS SINCE LAST PERIOD   🌙   EXPECT NEXT PERIOD AROUND_____

Day One of Cycle

- ❑ Backaches
- ❑ Sore Breasts
- ❑ Cravings
- ❑ Cramps
- ❑ Acne
- ❑ Other:_____

Sleep ☺ 😐 ☹
Energy ☺ 😐 ☹
Mood ☺ 😐 ☹

_____

_____

Day two of Cycle

- ❑ Backaches
- ❑ Sore Breasts
- ❑ Cravings
- ❑ Cramps
- ❑ Acne
- ❑ Other:_____

Sleep ☺ 😐 ☹
Energy ☺ 😐 ☹
Mood ☺ 😐 ☹

_____

_____

Day three of Cycle

- ❑ Backaches
- ❑ Sore Breasts
- ❑ Cravings
- ❑ Cramps
- ❑ Acne
- ❑ Other:_____

Sleep ☺ 😐 ☹
Energy ☺ 😐 ☹
Mood ☺ 😐 ☹

_____

_____

Year:_____

DAY FOUR OF CYCLE

❑ Backaches ❑ Cramps
❑ Sore Breasts ❑ Acne
❑ Cravings ❑ Other:_____

Sleep ☺ 😐 ☹
Energy ☺ 😐 ☹
Mood ☺ 😐 ☹

_____
_____
_____

DAY FIVE OF CYCLE

❑ Backaches ❑ Cramps
❑ Sore Breasts ❑ Acne
❑ Cravings ❑ Other:_____

Sleep ☺ 😐 ☹
Energy ☺ 😐 ☹
Mood ☺ 😐 ☹

_____
_____
_____

DAY SIX OF CYCLE

❑ Backaches ❑ Cramps
❑ Sore Breasts ❑ Acne
❑ Cravings ❑ Other:_____

Sleep ☺ 😐 ☹
Energy ☺ 😐 ☹
Mood ☺ 😐 ☹

_____
_____
_____

DAY SEVEN OF CYCLE

❑ Backaches ❑ Cramps
❑ Sore Breasts ❑ Acne
❑ Cravings ❑ Other:_____

Sleep ☺ 😐 ☹
Energy ☺ 😐 ☹
Mood ☺ 😐 ☹

_____
_____
_____

| J | F | M | A | M | J | J | A | S | O | N | D |

1	2	3	4	5	6	7	8	9	10	11	12
13	14	15	16	17	18	19	20	21	22	23	24
25	26	27	28	29	30	31	*Cross off dates that do not apply for this month				

KEY: ■ Heavy ◤ Medium △ Light • Spotting ⊠ N/A

_____ DAYS SINCE LAST PERIOD 🌙 EXPECT NEXT PERIOD AROUND_____

Day One of Cycle

❏ Backaches   ❏ Cramps
❏ Sore Breasts   ❏ Acne
❏ Cravings   ❏ Other:_____

Sleep ☺ 😐 ☹
Energy ☺ 😐 ☹
Mood ☺ 😐 ☹

_____

_____

_____

Day two of Cycle

❏ Backaches   ❏ Cramps
❏ Sore Breasts   ❏ Acne
❏ Cravings   ❏ Other:_____

Sleep ☺ 😐 ☹
Energy ☺ 😐 ☹
Mood ☺ 😐 ☹

_____

_____

_____

Day three of Cycle

❏ Backaches   ❏ Cramps
❏ Sore Breasts   ❏ Acne
❏ Cravings   ❏ Other:_____

Sleep ☺ 😐 ☹
Energy ☺ 😐 ☹
Mood ☺ 😐 ☹

_____

_____

_____

Year:_____

Day Four of Cycle

❑ Backaches ❑ Cramps   Sleep ☺ 😐 ☹
❑ Sore Breasts ❑ Acne   Energy ☺ 😐 ☹
❑ Cravings   ❑ Other:_____ Mood ☺ 😐 ☹

_____

_____

_____

Day Five of Cycle

❑ Backaches ❑ Cramps   Sleep ☺ 😐 ☹
❑ Sore Breasts ❑ Acne   Energy ☺ 😐 ☹
❑ Cravings   ❑ Other:_____ Mood ☺ 😐 ☹

_____

_____

_____

Day six of Cycle

❑ Backaches ❑ Cramps   Sleep ☺ 😐 ☹
❑ Sore Breasts ❑ Acne   Energy ☺ 😐 ☹
❑ Cravings   ❑ Other:_____ Mood ☺ 😐 ☹

_____

_____

_____

Day seven of Cycle

❑ Backaches ❑ Cramps   Sleep ☺ 😐 ☹
❑ Sore Breasts ❑ Acne   Energy ☺ 😐 ☹
❑ Cravings   ❑ Other:_____ Mood ☺ 😐 ☹

_____

_____

_____

| J | F | M | A | M | J | J | A | S | O | N | D |

1	2	3	4	5	6	7	8	9	10	11	12
13	14	15	16	17	18	19	20	21	22	23	24
25	26	27	28	29	30	31	*Cross off dates that do not apply for this month				

KEY: ■ Heavy ◨ Medium △ Light • Spotting ⊠ N/A

_____ DAYS SINCE LAST PERIOD 🌙 EXPECT NEXT PERIOD AROUND_____

Day One of Cycle

❏ Backaches ❏ Cramps
❏ Sore Breasts ❏ Acne
❏ Cravings ❏ Other:_____

Sleep ☺ 😐 ☹
Energy ☺ 😐 ☹
Mood ☺ 😐 ☹

_____

_____

_____

Day two of Cycle

❏ Backaches ❏ Cramps
❏ Sore Breasts ❏ Acne
❏ Cravings ❏ Other:_____

Sleep ☺ 😐 ☹
Energy ☺ 😐 ☹
Mood ☺ 😐 ☹

_____

_____

_____

Day three of Cycle

❏ Backaches ❏ Cramps
❏ Sore Breasts ❏ Acne
❏ Cravings ❏ Other:_____

Sleep ☺ 😐 ☹
Energy ☺ 😐 ☹
Mood ☺ 😐 ☹

_____

_____

_____

Day Four of Cycle

❏ Backaches   ❏ Cramps

❏ Sore Breasts ❏ Acne

❏ Cravings   ❏ Other:_____

Sleep ☺ 😐 ☹
Energy ☺ 😐 ☹
Mood ☺ 😐 ☹

_____

_____

_____

Day Five of Cycle

❏ Backaches   ❏ Cramps

❏ Sore Breasts ❏ Acne

❏ Cravings   ❏ Other:_____

Sleep ☺ 😐 ☹
Energy ☺ 😐 ☹
Mood ☺ 😐 ☹

_____

_____

_____

Day Six of Cycle

❏ Backaches   ❏ Cramps

❏ Sore Breasts ❏ Acne

❏ Cravings   ❏ Other:_____

Sleep ☺ 😐 ☹
Energy ☺ 😐 ☹
Mood ☺ 😐 ☹

_____

_____

_____

Day Seven of Cycle

❏ Backaches   ❏ Cramps

❏ Sore Breasts ❏ Acne

❏ Cravings   ❏ Other:_____

Sleep ☺ 😐 ☹
Energy ☺ 😐 ☹
Mood ☺ 😐 ☹

_____

_____

_____

| J | F | M | A | M | J | J | A | S | O | N | D |

1	2	3	4	5	6	7	8	9	10	11	12
13	14	15	16	17	18	19	20	21	22	23	24
25	26	27	28	29	30	31	*Cross off dates that do not apply for this month				

KEY: ■ Heavy ◢ Medium △ Light • Spotting ⊠ N/A

_____ DAYS SINCE LAST PERIOD 🌙 EXPECT NEXT PERIOD AROUND_____

DAY ONE OF CYCLE

❏ Backaches ❏ Cramps   Sleep ☺ 😐 ☹
❏ Sore Breasts ❏ Acne   Energy ☺ 😐 ☹
❏ Cravings ❏ Other:_____   Mood ☺ 😐 ☹

_____

_____

_____

DAY TWO OF CYCLE

❏ Backaches ❏ Cramps   Sleep ☺ 😐 ☹
❏ Sore Breasts ❏ Acne   Energy ☺ 😐 ☹
❏ Cravings ❏ Other:_____   Mood ☺ 😐 ☹

_____

_____

_____

DAY THREE OF CYCLE

❏ Backaches ❏ Cramps   Sleep ☺ 😐 ☹
❏ Sore Breasts ❏ Acne   Energy ☺ 😐 ☹
❏ Cravings ❏ Other:_____   Mood ☺ 😐 ☹

_____

_____

_____

Year:_____

Day Four of Cycle

❏ Backaches   ❏ Cramps   Sleep 🙂 😐 🙁
❏ Sore Breasts   ❏ Acne   Energy 🙂 😐 🙁
❏ Cravings   ❏ Other:_____   Mood 🙂 😐 🙁

_____

_____

_____

Day Five of Cycle

❏ Backaches   ❏ Cramps   Sleep 🙂 😐 🙁
❏ Sore Breasts   ❏ Acne   Energy 🙂 😐 🙁
❏ Cravings   ❏ Other:_____   Mood 🙂 😐 🙁

_____

_____

_____

Day Six of Cycle

❏ Backaches   ❏ Cramps   Sleep 🙂 😐 🙁
❏ Sore Breasts   ❏ Acne   Energy 🙂 😐 🙁
❏ Cravings   ❏ Other:_____   Mood 🙂 😐 🙁

_____

_____

_____

Day Seven of Cycle

❏ Backaches   ❏ Cramps   Sleep 🙂 😐 🙁
❏ Sore Breasts   ❏ Acne   Energy 🙂 😐 🙁
❏ Cravings   ❏ Other:_____   Mood 🙂 😐 🙁

_____

_____

_____

J	F	M	A	M	J	J	A	S	O	N	D

1	2	3	4	5	6	7	8	9	10	11	12
13	14	15	16	17	18	19	20	21	22	23	24
25	26	27	28	29	30	31	*Cross off dates that do not apply for this month				

KEY: ■ Heavy ◣ Medium △ Light • Spotting ⊠ N/A

_____ DAYS SINCE LAST PERIOD 🌙 EXPECT NEXT PERIOD AROUND_____

DAY ONE OF CYCLE

❑ Backaches ❑ Cramps
❑ Sore Breasts ❑ Acne
❑ Cravings ❑ Other:_____

Sleep ☺ 😐 ☹
Energy ☺ 😐 ☹
Mood ☺ 😐 ☹

_____

_____

_____

DAY TWO OF CYCLE

❑ Backaches ❑ Cramps
❑ Sore Breasts ❑ Acne
❑ Cravings ❑ Other:_____

Sleep ☺ 😐 ☹
Energy ☺ 😐 ☹
Mood ☺ 😐 ☹

_____

_____

_____

DAY THREE OF CYCLE

❑ Backaches ❑ Cramps
❑ Sore Breasts ❑ Acne
❑ Cravings ❑ Other:_____

Sleep ☺ 😐 ☹
Energy ☺ 😐 ☹
Mood ☺ 😐 ☹

_____

_____

_____

Year:_____

Day Four of Cycle

❑   Backaches   ❑   Cramps   Sleep   ☺   😐   ☹
❑   Sore Breasts   ❑   Acne   Energy   ☺   😐   ☹
❑   Cravings   ❑   Other:_____   Mood   ☺   😐   ☹

_____

_____

_____

Day Five of Cycle

❑   Backaches   ❑   Cramps   Sleep   ☺   😐   ☹
❑   Sore Breasts   ❑   Acne   Energy   ☺   😐   ☹
❑   Cravings   ❑   Other:_____   Mood   ☺   😐   ☹

_____

_____

_____

Day six of Cycle

❑   Backaches   ❑   Cramps   Sleep   ☺   😐   ☹
❑   Sore Breasts   ❑   Acne   Energy   ☺   😐   ☹
❑   Cravings   ❑   Other:_____   Mood   ☺   😐   ☹

_____

_____

_____

Day seven of Cycle

❑   Backaches   ❑   Cramps   Sleep   ☺   😐   ☹
❑   Sore Breasts   ❑   Acne   Energy   ☺   😐   ☹
❑   Cravings   ❑   Other:_____   Mood   ☺   😐   ☹

_____

_____

_____

| J | F | M | A | M | J | J | A | S | O | N | D |

1	2	3	4	5	6	7	8	9	10	11	12
13	14	15	16	17	18	19	20	21	22	23	24
25	26	27	28	29	30	31	*Cross off dates that do not apply for this month				

KEY: ■ Heavy ◤ Medium △ Light • Spotting ⊠ N/A

_____ DAYS SINCE LAST PERIOD 🌙 EXPECT NEXT PERIOD AROUND_____

DAY ONE OF CYCLE

❑ Backaches ❑ Cramps
❑ Sore Breasts ❑ Acne
❑ Cravings ❑ Other:_____

Sleep ☺ 😐 ☹
Energy ☺ 😐 ☹
Mood ☺ 😐 ☹

_____

_____

_____

DAY TWO OF CYCLE

❑ Backaches ❑ Cramps
❑ Sore Breasts ❑ Acne
❑ Cravings ❑ Other:_____

Sleep ☺ 😐 ☹
Energy ☺ 😐 ☹
Mood ☺ 😐 ☹

_____

_____

_____

DAY THREE OF CYCLE

❑ Backaches ❑ Cramps
❑ Sore Breasts ❑ Acne
❑ Cravings ❑ Other:_____

Sleep ☺ 😐 ☹
Energy ☺ 😐 ☹
Mood ☺ 😐 ☹

_____

_____

Year:_____

Day Four of Cycle

- ❏ Backaches
- ❏ Sore Breasts
- ❏ Cravings

- ❏ Cramps
- ❏ Acne
- ❏ Other:_____

Sleep ☺ 😐 ☹
Energy ☺ 😐 ☹
Mood ☺ 😐 ☹

_____

_____

_____

Day Five of Cycle

- ❏ Backaches
- ❏ Sore Breasts
- ❏ Cravings

- ❏ Cramps
- ❏ Acne
- ❏ Other:_____

Sleep ☺ 😐 ☹
Energy ☺ 😐 ☹
Mood ☺ 😐 ☹

_____

_____

_____

Day Six of Cycle

- ❏ Backaches
- ❏ Sore Breasts
- ❏ Cravings

- ❏ Cramps
- ❏ Acne
- ❏ Other:_____

Sleep ☺ 😐 ☹
Energy ☺ 😐 ☹
Mood ☺ 😐 ☹

_____

_____

_____

Day Seven of Cycle

- ❏ Backaches
- ❏ Sore Breasts
- ❏ Cravings

- ❏ Cramps
- ❏ Acne
- ❏ Other:_____

Sleep ☺ 😐 ☹
Energy ☺ 😐 ☹
Mood ☺ 😐 ☹

_____

_____

_____

| J | F | M | A | M | J | J | A | S | O | N | D |

1	2	3	4	5	6	7	8	9	10	11	12
13	14	15	16	17	18	19	20	21	22	23	24
25	26	27	28	29	30	31	*Cross off dates that do not apply for this month				

KEY: ■ Heavy ◣ Medium △ Light • Spotting ⊠ N/A

_____ DAYS SINCE LAST PERIOD 🌙 EXPECT NEXT PERIOD AROUND_____

DAY ONE OF CYCLE

❏ Backaches ❏ Cramps
❏ Sore Breasts ❏ Acne
❏ Cravings ❏ Other:_____

Sleep ☺ 😐 ☹
Energy ☺ 😐 ☹
Mood ☺ 😐 ☹

_____

_____

DAY TWO OF CYCLE

❏ Backaches ❏ Cramps
❏ Sore Breasts ❏ Acne
❏ Cravings ❏ Other:_____

Sleep ☺ 😐 ☹
Energy ☺ 😐 ☹
Mood ☺ 😐 ☹

_____

_____

DAY THREE OF CYCLE

❏ Backaches ❏ Cramps
❏ Sore Breasts ❏ Acne
❏ Cravings ❏ Other:_____

Sleep ☺ 😐 ☹
Energy ☺ 😐 ☹
Mood ☺ 😐 ☹

_____

_____

DAY FOUR OF CYCLE

❑ Backaches ❑ Cramps   Sleep ☺ 😐 ☹
❑ Sore Breasts ❑ Acne   Energy ☺ 😐 ☹
❑ Cravings   ❑ Other:_____ Mood ☺ 😐 ☹

_____

_____

_____

DAY FIVE OF CYCLE

❑ Backaches ❑ Cramps   Sleep ☺ 😐 ☹
❑ Sore Breasts ❑ Acne   Energy ☺ 😐 ☹
❑ Cravings   ❑ Other:_____ Mood ☺ 😐 ☹

_____

_____

_____

DAY SIX OF CYCLE

❑ Backaches ❑ Cramps   Sleep ☺ 😐 ☹
❑ Sore Breasts ❑ Acne   Energy ☺ 😐 ☹
❑ Cravings   ❑ Other:_____ Mood ☺ 😐 ☹

_____

_____

_____

DAY SEVEN OF CYCLE

❑ Backaches ❑ Cramps   Sleep ☺ 😐 ☹
❑ Sore Breasts ❑ Acne   Energy ☺ 😐 ☹
❑ Cravings   ❑ Other:_____ Mood ☺ 😐 ☹

_____

_____

_____

| J | F | M | A | M | J | J | A | S | O | N | D |

1	2	3	4	5	6	7	8	9	10	11	12
13	14	15	16	17	18	19	20	21	22	23	24
25	26	27	28	29	30	31	*Cross off dates that do not apply for this month				

KEY: ■ Heavy ◣ Medium △ Light • Spotting ⊠ N/A

_____ DAYS SINCE LAST PERIOD 🌙 EXPECT NEXT PERIOD AROUND_____

Day One of Cycle

❏ Backaches ❏ Cramps
❏ Sore Breasts ❏ Acne
❏ Cravings ❏ Other:_____

Sleep ☺ 😐 ☹
Energy ☺ 😐 ☹
Mood ☺ 😐 ☹

_____

_____

_____

Day two of Cycle

❏ Backaches ❏ Cramps
❏ Sore Breasts ❏ Acne
❏ Cravings ❏ Other:_____

Sleep ☺ 😐 ☹
Energy ☺ 😐 ☹
Mood ☺ 😐 ☹

_____

_____

_____

Day three of Cycle

❏ Backaches ❏ Cramps
❏ Sore Breasts ❏ Acne
❏ Cravings ❏ Other:_____

Sleep ☺ 😐 ☹
Energy ☺ 😐 ☹
Mood ☺ 😐 ☹

_____

_____

Day Four of Cycle

❑ Backaches ❑ Cramps Sleep 🙂 😐 🙁
❑ Sore Breasts ❑ Acne Energy 🙂 😐 🙁
❑ Cravings ❑ Other:_____ Mood 🙂 😐 🙁

_____

_____

_____

Day Five of Cycle

❑ Backaches ❑ Cramps Sleep 🙂 😐 🙁
❑ Sore Breasts ❑ Acne Energy 🙂 😐 🙁
❑ Cravings ❑ Other:_____ Mood 🙂 😐 🙁

_____

_____

_____

Day Six of Cycle

❑ Backaches ❑ Cramps Sleep 🙂 😐 🙁
❑ Sore Breasts ❑ Acne Energy 🙂 😐 🙁
❑ Cravings ❑ Other:_____ Mood 🙂 😐 🙁

_____

_____

_____

Day Seven of Cycle

❑ Backaches ❑ Cramps Sleep 🙂 😐 🙁
❑ Sore Breasts ❑ Acne Energy 🙂 😐 🙁
❑ Cravings ❑ Other:_____ Mood 🙂 😐 🙁

_____

_____

_____

| J | F | M | A | M | J | J | A | S | O | N | D |

1	2	3	4	5	6	7	8	9	10	11	12
13	14	15	16	17	18	19	20	21	22	23	24
25	26	27	28	29	30	31	*Cross off dates that do not apply for this month				

KEY: ■ Heavy ◢ Medium △ Light • Spotting ⊠ N/A

_____ DAYS SINCE LAST PERIOD 🌙 EXPECT NEXT PERIOD AROUND_____

DAY ONE OF CYCLE

❑ Backaches ❑ Cramps
❑ Sore Breasts ❑ Acne
❑ Cravings ❑ Other:_____

Sleep ☺ 😐 ☹
Energy ☺ 😐 ☹
Mood ☺ 😐 ☹

_____

_____

_____

DAY TWO OF CYCLE

❑ Backaches ❑ Cramps
❑ Sore Breasts ❑ Acne
❑ Cravings ❑ Other:_____

Sleep ☺ 😐 ☹
Energy ☺ 😐 ☹
Mood ☺ 😐 ☹

_____

_____

_____

DAY THREE OF CYCLE

❑ Backaches ❑ Cramps
❑ Sore Breasts ❑ Acne
❑ Cravings ❑ Other:_____

Sleep ☺ 😐 ☹
Energy ☺ 😐 ☹
Mood ☺ 😐 ☹

_____

_____

Day Four of Cycle

- ❏ Backaches
- ❏ Sore Breasts
- ❏ Cravings

- ❏ Cramps
- ❏ Acne
- ❏ Other:_____

Sleep ☺ 😐 ☹
Energy ☺ 😐 ☹
Mood ☺ 😐 ☹

_____

_____

_____

Day Five of Cycle

- ❏ Backaches
- ❏ Sore Breasts
- ❏ Cravings

- ❏ Cramps
- ❏ Acne
- ❏ Other:_____

Sleep ☺ 😐 ☹
Energy ☺ 😐 ☹
Mood ☺ 😐 ☹

_____

_____

_____

Day six of Cycle

- ❏ Backaches
- ❏ Sore Breasts
- ❏ Cravings

- ❏ Cramps
- ❏ Acne
- ❏ Other:_____

Sleep ☺ 😐 ☹
Energy ☺ 😐 ☹
Mood ☺ 😐 ☹

_____

_____

_____

Day seven of Cycle

- ❏ Backaches
- ❏ Sore Breasts
- ❏ Cravings

- ❏ Cramps
- ❏ Acne
- ❏ Other:_____

Sleep ☺ 😐 ☹
Energy ☺ 😐 ☹
Mood ☺ 😐 ☹

_____

_____

_____

| J | F | M | A | M | J | J | A | S | O | N | D |

1	2	3	4	5	6	7	8	9	10	11	12
13	14	15	16	17	18	19	20	21	22	23	24
25	26	27	28	29	30	31	*Cross off dates that do not apply for this month					

KEY: ■ Heavy ◨ Medium △ Light • Spotting ⊠ N/A

_____ DAYS SINCE LAST PERIOD 🌙 EXPECT NEXT PERIOD AROUND_____

DAY ONE OF CYCLE

❏ Backaches ❏ Cramps
❏ Sore Breasts ❏ Acne
❏ Cravings ❏ Other:_____

Sleep ☺ 😐 ☹
Energy ☺ 😐 ☹
Mood ☺ 😐 ☹

_____
_____
_____

DAY TWO OF CYCLE

❏ Backaches ❏ Cramps
❏ Sore Breasts ❏ Acne
❏ Cravings ❏ Other:_____

Sleep ☺ 😐 ☹
Energy ☺ 😐 ☹
Mood ☺ 😐 ☹

_____
_____
_____

DAY THREE OF CYCLE

❏ Backaches ❏ Cramps
❏ Sore Breasts ❏ Acne
❏ Cravings ❏ Other:_____

Sleep ☺ 😐 ☹
Energy ☺ 😐 ☹
Mood ☺ 😐 ☹

_____
_____
_____

Day Four of Cycle

❏ Backaches ❏ Cramps Sleep ☺ 😐 ☹
❏ Sore Breasts ❏ Acne Energy ☺ 😐 ☹
❏ Cravings ❏ Other:_____ Mood ☺ 😐 ☹

_____

_____

_____

Day Five of Cycle

❏ Backaches ❏ Cramps Sleep ☺ 😐 ☹
❏ Sore Breasts ❏ Acne Energy ☺ 😐 ☹
❏ Cravings ❏ Other:_____ Mood ☺ 😐 ☹

_____

_____

_____

Day six of Cycle

❏ Backaches ❏ Cramps Sleep ☺ 😐 ☹
❏ Sore Breasts ❏ Acne Energy ☺ 😐 ☹
❏ Cravings ❏ Other:_____ Mood ☺ 😐 ☹

_____

_____

_____

Day seven of Cycle

❏ Backaches ❏ Cramps Sleep ☺ 😐 ☹
❏ Sore Breasts ❏ Acne Energy ☺ 😐 ☹
❏ Cravings ❏ Other:_____ Mood ☺ 😐 ☹

_____

_____

_____

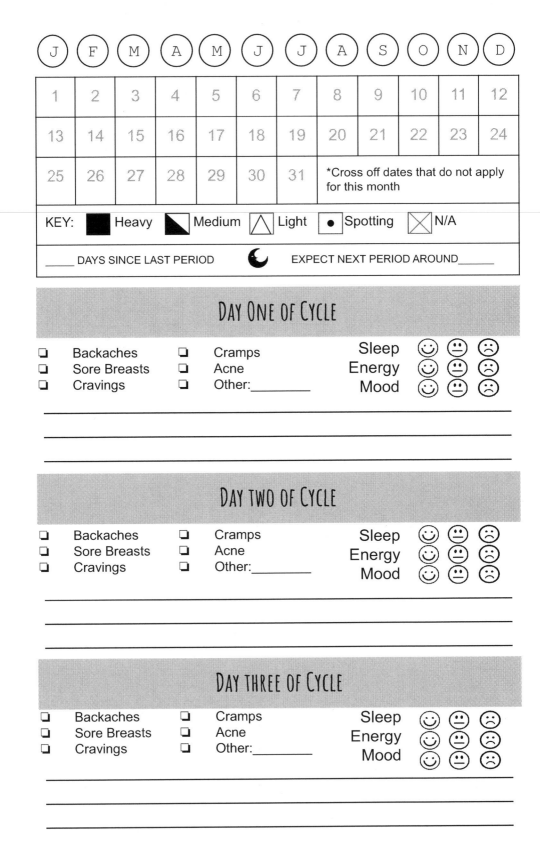

| J | F | M | A | M | J | J | A | S | O | N | D |

1	2	3	4	5	6	7	8	9	10	11	12
13	14	15	16	17	18	19	20	21	22	23	24
25	26	27	28	29	30	31	*Cross off dates that do not apply for this month				

KEY: ■ Heavy ◣ Medium △ Light • Spotting ⊠ N/A

_____ DAYS SINCE LAST PERIOD 🌙 EXPECT NEXT PERIOD AROUND_____

Day One of Cycle

❏ Backaches ❏ Cramps
❏ Sore Breasts ❏ Acne
❏ Cravings ❏ Other:_____

Sleep ☺ 😐 ☹
Energy ☺ 😐 ☹
Mood ☺ 😐 ☹

_____

_____

_____

Day two of Cycle

❏ Backaches ❏ Cramps
❏ Sore Breasts ❏ Acne
❏ Cravings ❏ Other:_____

Sleep ☺ 😐 ☹
Energy ☺ 😐 ☹
Mood ☺ 😐 ☹

_____

_____

_____

Day three of Cycle

❏ Backaches ❏ Cramps
❏ Sore Breasts ❏ Acne
❏ Cravings ❏ Other:_____

Sleep ☺ 😐 ☹
Energy ☺ 😐 ☹
Mood ☺ 😐 ☹

_____

_____

_____

Day Four of Cycle

❏ Backaches ❏ Cramps Sleep ☺ 😐 ☹
❏ Sore Breasts ❏ Acne Energy ☺ 😐 ☹
❏ Cravings ❏ Other:_____ Mood ☺ 😐 ☹

_____

_____

_____

Day Five of Cycle

❏ Backaches ❏ Cramps Sleep ☺ 😐 ☹
❏ Sore Breasts ❏ Acne Energy ☺ 😐 ☹
❏ Cravings ❏ Other:_____ Mood ☺ 😐 ☹

_____

_____

_____

Day Six of Cycle

❏ Backaches ❏ Cramps Sleep ☺ 😐 ☹
❏ Sore Breasts ❏ Acne Energy ☺ 😐 ☹
❏ Cravings ❏ Other:_____ Mood ☺ 😐 ☹

_____

_____

_____

Day Seven of Cycle

❏ Backaches ❏ Cramps Sleep ☺ 😐 ☹
❏ Sore Breasts ❏ Acne Energy ☺ 😐 ☹
❏ Cravings ❏ Other:_____ Mood ☺ 😐 ☹

_____

_____

_____

| J | F | M | A | M | J | J | A | S | O | N | D |

1	2	3	4	5	6	7	8	9	10	11	12
13	14	15	16	17	18	19	20	21	22	23	24
25	26	27	28	29	30	31	*Cross off dates that do not apply for this month				

KEY: ■ Heavy ◣ Medium △ Light • Spotting ⊠ N/A

_____ DAYS SINCE LAST PERIOD ☾ EXPECT NEXT PERIOD AROUND_____

Day One of Cycle

❏ Backaches ❏ Cramps Sleep ☺ ☺ ☹
❏ Sore Breasts ❏ Acne Energy ☺ ☺ ☹
❏ Cravings ❏ Other:_____ Mood ☺ ☺ ☹

_____

_____

_____

Day two of Cycle

❏ Backaches ❏ Cramps Sleep ☺ ☺ ☹
❏ Sore Breasts ❏ Acne Energy ☺ ☺ ☹
❏ Cravings ❏ Other:_____ Mood ☺ ☺ ☹

_____

_____

_____

Day three of Cycle

❏ Backaches ❏ Cramps Sleep ☺ ☺ ☹
❏ Sore Breasts ❏ Acne Energy ☺ ☺ ☹
❏ Cravings ❏ Other:_____ Mood ☺ ☺ ☹

_____

_____

_____

Year:_____

Day Four of Cycle

- ❏ Backaches
- ❏ Sore Breasts
- ❏ Cravings
- ❏ Cramps
- ❏ Acne
- ❏ Other:_____

Sleep ☺ 😐 ☹
Energy ☺ 😐 ☹
Mood ☺ 😐 ☹

_____

_____

_____

Day Five of Cycle

- ❏ Backaches
- ❏ Sore Breasts
- ❏ Cravings
- ❏ Cramps
- ❏ Acne
- ❏ Other:_____

Sleep ☺ 😐 ☹
Energy ☺ 😐 ☹
Mood ☺ 😐 ☹

_____

_____

_____

Day Six of Cycle

- ❏ Backaches
- ❏ Sore Breasts
- ❏ Cravings
- ❏ Cramps
- ❏ Acne
- ❏ Other:_____

Sleep ☺ 😐 ☹
Energy ☺ 😐 ☹
Mood ☺ 😐 ☹

_____

_____

_____

Day Seven of Cycle

- ❏ Backaches
- ❏ Sore Breasts
- ❏ Cravings
- ❏ Cramps
- ❏ Acne
- ❏ Other:_____

Sleep ☺ 😐 ☹
Energy ☺ 😐 ☹
Mood ☺ 😐 ☹

_____

_____

_____

| J | F | M | A | M | J | J | A | S | O | N | D |

1	2	3	4	5	6	7	8	9	10	11	12
13	14	15	16	17	18	19	20	21	22	23	24
25	26	27	28	29	30	31	*Cross off dates that do not apply for this month				

KEY: ■ Heavy ◤ Medium △ Light • Spotting ⊠ N/A

_____ DAYS SINCE LAST PERIOD ☾ EXPECT NEXT PERIOD AROUND_____

Day One of Cycle

❑ Backaches ❑ Cramps Sleep ☺ 😐 ☹
❑ Sore Breasts ❑ Acne Energy ☺ 😐 ☹
❑ Cravings ❑ Other:_____ Mood ☺ 😐 ☹

_____

_____

_____

Day two of Cycle

❑ Backaches ❑ Cramps Sleep ☺ 😐 ☹
❑ Sore Breasts ❑ Acne Energy ☺ 😐 ☹
❑ Cravings ❑ Other:_____ Mood ☺ 😐 ☹

_____

_____

_____

Day three of Cycle

❑ Backaches ❑ Cramps Sleep ☺ 😐 ☹
❑ Sore Breasts ❑ Acne Energy ☺ 😐 ☹
❑ Cravings ❑ Other:_____ Mood ☺ 😐 ☹

_____

_____

_____

Day Four of Cycle

❑ Backaches   ❑ Cramps   Sleep ☺ 😐 ☹
❑ Sore Breasts   ❑ Acne   Energy ☺ 😐 ☹
❑ Cravings   ❑ Other:_____ Mood ☺ 😐 ☹

_____

_____

_____

Day Five of Cycle

❑ Backaches   ❑ Cramps   Sleep ☺ 😐 ☹
❑ Sore Breasts   ❑ Acne   Energy ☺ 😐 ☹
❑ Cravings   ❑ Other:_____ Mood ☺ 😐 ☹

_____

_____

_____

Day Six of Cycle

❑ Backaches   ❑ Cramps   Sleep ☺ 😐 ☹
❑ Sore Breasts   ❑ Acne   Energy ☺ 😐 ☹
❑ Cravings   ❑ Other:_____ Mood ☺ 😐 ☹

_____

_____

_____

Day Seven of Cycle

❑ Backaches   ❑ Cramps   Sleep ☺ 😐 ☹
❑ Sore Breasts   ❑ Acne   Energy ☺ 😐 ☹
❑ Cravings   ❑ Other:_____ Mood ☺ 😐 ☹

_____

_____

| J | F | M | A | M | J | J | A | S | O | N | D |

1	2	3	4	5	6	7	8	9	10	11	12
13	14	15	16	17	18	19	20	21	22	23	24
25	26	27	28	29	30	31	*Cross off dates that do not apply for this month				

KEY: ■ Heavy ◥ Medium △ Light • Spotting ⊠ N/A

_____ DAYS SINCE LAST PERIOD 🌙 EXPECT NEXT PERIOD AROUND_____

Day One of Cycle

❑ Backaches ❑ Cramps
❑ Sore Breasts ❑ Acne
❑ Cravings ❑ Other:_____

Sleep ☺ 😐 ☹
Energy ☺ 😐 ☹
Mood ☺ 😐 ☹

_____

_____

Day two of Cycle

❑ Backaches ❑ Cramps
❑ Sore Breasts ❑ Acne
❑ Cravings ❑ Other:_____

Sleep ☺ 😐 ☹
Energy ☺ 😐 ☹
Mood ☺ 😐 ☹

_____

_____

Day three of Cycle

❑ Backaches ❑ Cramps
❑ Sore Breasts ❑ Acne
❑ Cravings ❑ Other:_____

Sleep ☺ 😐 ☹
Energy ☺ 😐 ☹
Mood ☺ 😐 ☹

_____

_____

Day Four of Cycle

- ❏ Backaches
- ❏ Sore Breasts
- ❏ Cravings

- ❏ Cramps
- ❏ Acne
- ❏ Other:_____

Sleep ☺ 😐 ☹
Energy ☺ 😐 ☹
Mood ☺ 😐 ☹

_____

_____

_____

Day Five of Cycle

- ❏ Backaches
- ❏ Sore Breasts
- ❏ Cravings

- ❏ Cramps
- ❏ Acne
- ❏ Other:_____

Sleep ☺ 😐 ☹
Energy ☺ 😐 ☹
Mood ☺ 😐 ☹

_____

_____

_____

Day Six of Cycle

- ❏ Backaches
- ❏ Sore Breasts
- ❏ Cravings

- ❏ Cramps
- ❏ Acne
- ❏ Other:_____

Sleep ☺ 😐 ☹
Energy ☺ 😐 ☹
Mood ☺ 😐 ☹

_____

_____

_____

Day Seven of Cycle

- ❏ Backaches
- ❏ Sore Breasts
- ❏ Cravings

- ❏ Cramps
- ❏ Acne
- ❏ Other:_____

Sleep ☺ 😐 ☹
Energy ☺ 😐 ☹
Mood ☺ 😐 ☹

_____

_____

_____

| J | F | M | A | M | J | J | A | S | O | N | D |

1	2	3	4	5	6	7	8	9	10	11	12
13	14	15	16	17	18	19	20	21	22	23	24
25	26	27	28	29	30	31	*Cross off dates that do not apply for this month				

KEY: ■ Heavy ◣ Medium △ Light • Spotting ⊠ N/A

_____ DAYS SINCE LAST PERIOD 🌙 EXPECT NEXT PERIOD AROUND_____

Day One of Cycle

❏ Backaches ❏ Cramps Sleep ☺ 😐 ☹
❏ Sore Breasts ❏ Acne Energy ☺ 😐 ☹
❏ Cravings ❏ Other:_____ Mood ☺ 😐 ☹

_____

_____

Day two of Cycle

❏ Backaches ❏ Cramps Sleep ☺ 😐 ☹
❏ Sore Breasts ❏ Acne Energy ☺ 😐 ☹
❏ Cravings ❏ Other:_____ Mood ☺ 😐 ☹

_____

_____

Day three of Cycle

❏ Backaches ❏ Cramps Sleep ☺ 😐 ☹
❏ Sore Breasts ❏ Acne Energy ☺ 😐 ☹
❏ Cravings ❏ Other:_____ Mood ☺ 😐 ☹

_____

_____

Day Four of Cycle

❑ Backaches ❑ Cramps
❑ Sore Breasts ❑ Acne
❑ Cravings ❑ Other:_____

Sleep 🙂 😐 🙁
Energy 🙂 😐 🙁
Mood 🙂 😐 🙁

_____

_____

_____

Day Five of Cycle

❑ Backaches ❑ Cramps
❑ Sore Breasts ❑ Acne
❑ Cravings ❑ Other:_____

Sleep 🙂 😐 🙁
Energy 🙂 😐 🙁
Mood 🙂 😐 🙁

_____

_____

_____

Day six of Cycle

❑ Backaches ❑ Cramps
❑ Sore Breasts ❑ Acne
❑ Cravings ❑ Other:_____

Sleep 🙂 😐 🙁
Energy 🙂 😐 🙁
Mood 🙂 😐 🙁

_____

_____

_____

Day seven of Cycle

❑ Backaches ❑ Cramps
❑ Sore Breasts ❑ Acne
❑ Cravings ❑ Other:_____

Sleep 🙂 😐 🙁
Energy 🙂 😐 🙁
Mood 🙂 😐 🙁

_____

_____

_____

| J | F | M | A | M | J | J | A | S | O | N | D |

1	2	3	4	5	6	7	8	9	10	11	12
13	14	15	16	17	18	19	20	21	22	23	24
25	26	27	28	29	30	31	*Cross off dates that do not apply for this month				

KEY: ■ Heavy ◣ Medium △ Light • Spotting ⊠ N/A

_____ DAYS SINCE LAST PERIOD 🌙 EXPECT NEXT PERIOD AROUND_____

Day One of Cycle

❑ Backaches   ❑ Cramps   Sleep ☺ 😐 ☹
❑ Sore Breasts ❑ Acne   Energy ☺ 😐 ☹
❑ Cravings   ❑ Other:_____ Mood ☺ 😐 ☹

_____

_____

_____

Day two of Cycle

❑ Backaches   ❑ Cramps   Sleep ☺ 😐 ☹
❑ Sore Breasts ❑ Acne   Energy ☺ 😐 ☹
❑ Cravings   ❑ Other:_____ Mood ☺ 😐 ☹

_____

_____

_____

Day three of Cycle

❑ Backaches   ❑ Cramps   Sleep ☺ 😐 ☹
❑ Sore Breasts ❑ Acne   Energy ☺ 😐 ☹
❑ Cravings   ❑ Other:_____ Mood ☺ 😐 ☹

_____

_____

_____

Day Four of Cycle

❏ Backaches ❏ Cramps Sleep ☺ 😐 ☹
❏ Sore Breasts ❏ Acne Energy ☺ 😐 ☹
❏ Cravings ❏ Other:_____ Mood ☺ 😐 ☹

_____

_____

_____

Day Five of Cycle

❏ Backaches ❏ Cramps Sleep ☺ 😐 ☹
❏ Sore Breasts ❏ Acne Energy ☺ 😐 ☹
❏ Cravings ❏ Other:_____ Mood ☺ 😐 ☹

_____

_____

_____

Day Six of Cycle

❏ Backaches ❏ Cramps Sleep ☺ 😐 ☹
❏ Sore Breasts ❏ Acne Energy ☺ 😐 ☹
❏ Cravings ❏ Other:_____ Mood ☺ 😐 ☹

_____

_____

_____

Day Seven of Cycle

❏ Backaches ❏ Cramps Sleep ☺ 😐 ☹
❏ Sore Breasts ❏ Acne Energy ☺ 😐 ☹
❏ Cravings ❏ Other:_____ Mood ☺ 😐 ☹

_____

_____

_____

| J | F | M | A | M | J | J | A | S | O | N | D |

1	2	3	4	5	6	7	8	9	10	11	12
13	14	15	16	17	18	19	20	21	22	23	24
25	26	27	28	29	30	31	*Cross off dates that do not apply for this month				

KEY: ■ Heavy ◨ Medium △ Light • Spotting ⊠ N/A

_____ DAYS SINCE LAST PERIOD 🌙 EXPECT NEXT PERIOD AROUND_____

Day One of Cycle

❏ Backaches ❏ Cramps Sleep ☺ 😐 ☹
❏ Sore Breasts ❏ Acne Energy ☺ 😐 ☹
❏ Cravings ❏ Other:_____ Mood ☺ 😐 ☹

_____

_____

_____

Day two of Cycle

❏ Backaches ❏ Cramps Sleep ☺ 😐 ☹
❏ Sore Breasts ❏ Acne Energy ☺ 😐 ☹
❏ Cravings ❏ Other:_____ Mood ☺ 😐 ☹

_____

_____

_____

Day three of Cycle

❏ Backaches ❏ Cramps Sleep ☺ 😐 ☹
❏ Sore Breasts ❏ Acne Energy ☺ 😐 ☹
❏ Cravings ❏ Other:_____ Mood ☺ 😐 ☹

_____

_____

_____

Year:_____

Day Four of Cycle

❑ Backaches ❑ Cramps Sleep ☺ 😐 ☹
❑ Sore Breasts ❑ Acne Energy ☺ 😐 ☹
❑ Cravings ❑ Other:_____ Mood ☺ 😐 ☹

_____

_____

_____

Day Five of Cycle

❑ Backaches ❑ Cramps Sleep ☺ 😐 ☹
❑ Sore Breasts ❑ Acne Energy ☺ 😐 ☹
❑ Cravings ❑ Other:_____ Mood ☺ 😐 ☹

_____

_____

_____

Day six of Cycle

❑ Backaches ❑ Cramps Sleep ☺ 😐 ☹
❑ Sore Breasts ❑ Acne Energy ☺ 😐 ☹
❑ Cravings ❑ Other:_____ Mood ☺ 😐 ☹

_____

_____

_____

Day seven of Cycle

❑ Backaches ❑ Cramps Sleep ☺ 😐 ☹
❑ Sore Breasts ❑ Acne Energy ☺ 😐 ☹
❑ Cravings ❑ Other:_____ Mood ☺ 😐 ☹

_____

_____

_____

| J | F | M | A | M | J | J | A | S | O | N | D |

1	2	3	4	5	6	7	8	9	10	11	12
13	14	15	16	17	18	19	20	21	22	23	24
25	26	27	28	29	30	31	*Cross off dates that do not apply for this month				

KEY: ■ Heavy ◢ Medium △ Light • Spotting ⊠ N/A

_____ DAYS SINCE LAST PERIOD 🌙 EXPECT NEXT PERIOD AROUND_____

DAY ONE OF CYCLE

❑ Backaches ❑ Cramps Sleep ☺ 😐 ☹
❑ Sore Breasts ❑ Acne Energy ☺ 😐 ☹
❑ Cravings ❑ Other:_____ Mood ☺ 😐 ☹

_____

_____

_____

DAY TWO OF CYCLE

❑ Backaches ❑ Cramps Sleep ☺ 😐 ☹
❑ Sore Breasts ❑ Acne Energy ☺ 😐 ☹
❑ Cravings ❑ Other:_____ Mood ☺ 😐 ☹

_____

_____

_____

DAY THREE OF CYCLE

❑ Backaches ❑ Cramps Sleep ☺ 😐 ☹
❑ Sore Breasts ❑ Acne Energy ☺ 😐 ☹
❑ Cravings ❑ Other:_____ Mood ☺ 😐 ☹

_____

_____

_____

Year:_____

Day Four of Cycle

❑ Backaches   ❑ Cramps   Sleep ☺ 😐 ☹
❑ Sore Breasts   ❑ Acne   Energy ☺ 😐 ☹
❑ Cravings   ❑ Other:_____   Mood ☺ 😐 ☹

_____

_____

_____

Day Five of Cycle

❑ Backaches   ❑ Cramps   Sleep ☺ 😐 ☹
❑ Sore Breasts   ❑ Acne   Energy ☺ 😐 ☹
❑ Cravings   ❑ Other:_____   Mood ☺ 😐 ☹

_____

_____

_____

Day six of Cycle

❑ Backaches   ❑ Cramps   Sleep ☺ 😐 ☹
❑ Sore Breasts   ❑ Acne   Energy ☺ 😐 ☹
❑ Cravings   ❑ Other:_____   Mood ☺ 😐 ☹

_____

_____

_____

Day seven of Cycle

❑ Backaches   ❑ Cramps   Sleep ☺ 😐 ☹
❑ Sore Breasts   ❑ Acne   Energy ☺ 😐 ☹
❑ Cravings   ❑ Other:_____   Mood ☺ 😐 ☹

_____

_____

_____

J	F	M	A	M	J	J	A	S	O	N	D

1	2	3	4	5	6	7	8	9	10	11	12
13	14	15	16	17	18	19	20	21	22	23	24
25	26	27	28	29	30	31	*Cross off dates that do not apply for this month				

KEY: ■ Heavy ◣ Medium △ Light • Spotting ⊠ N/A

_____ DAYS SINCE LAST PERIOD 🌙 EXPECT NEXT PERIOD AROUND_____

Day One of Cycle

❏ Backaches ❏ Cramps
❏ Sore Breasts ❏ Acne
❏ Cravings ❏ Other:_____

Sleep ☺ 😐 ☹
Energy ☺ 😐 ☹
Mood ☺ 😐 ☹

_____

_____

Day two of Cycle

❏ Backaches ❏ Cramps
❏ Sore Breasts ❏ Acne
❏ Cravings ❏ Other:_____

Sleep ☺ 😐 ☹
Energy ☺ 😐 ☹
Mood ☺ 😐 ☹

_____

_____

Day three of Cycle

❏ Backaches ❏ Cramps
❏ Sore Breasts ❏ Acne
❏ Cravings ❏ Other:_____

Sleep ☺ 😐 ☹
Energy ☺ 😐 ☹
Mood ☺ 😐 ☹

_____

_____

Year:_____

Day Four of Cycle

❏ Backaches ❏ Cramps Sleep 😊 😐 ☹
❏ Sore Breasts ❏ Acne Energy 😊 😐 ☹
❏ Cravings ❏ Other:_____ Mood 😊 😐 ☹

_____

_____

_____

Day Five of Cycle

❏ Backaches ❏ Cramps Sleep 😊 😐 ☹
❏ Sore Breasts ❏ Acne Energy 😊 😐 ☹
❏ Cravings ❏ Other:_____ Mood 😊 😐 ☹

_____

_____

_____

Day six of Cycle

❏ Backaches ❏ Cramps Sleep 😊 😐 ☹
❏ Sore Breasts ❏ Acne Energy 😊 😐 ☹
❏ Cravings ❏ Other:_____ Mood 😊 😐 ☹

_____

_____

_____

Day seven of Cycle

❏ Backaches ❏ Cramps Sleep 😊 😐 ☹
❏ Sore Breasts ❏ Acne Energy 😊 😐 ☹
❏ Cravings ❏ Other:_____ Mood 😊 😐 ☹

_____

_____

_____

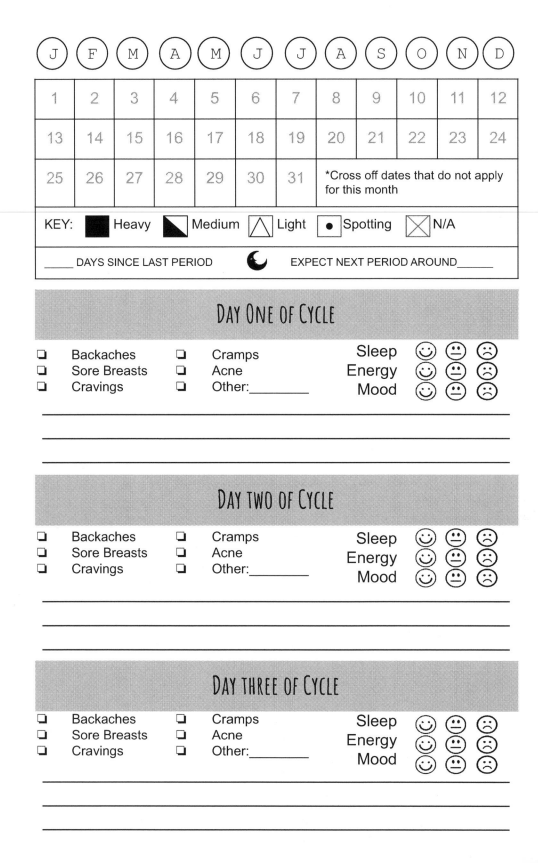

| J | F | M | A | M | J | J | A | S | O | N | D |

1	2	3	4	5	6	7	8	9	10	11	12
13	14	15	16	17	18	19	20	21	22	23	24
25	26	27	28	29	30	31	*Cross off dates that do not apply for this month				

KEY: ■ Heavy ◣ Medium △ Light • Spotting ⊠ N/A

_____ DAYS SINCE LAST PERIOD 🌙 EXPECT NEXT PERIOD AROUND_____

DAY ONE OF CYCLE

❑ Backaches ❑ Cramps
❑ Sore Breasts ❑ Acne
❑ Cravings ❑ Other:_____

Sleep ☺ 😐 ☹
Energy ☺ 😐 ☹
Mood ☺ 😐 ☹

_____

_____

_____

DAY TWO OF CYCLE

❑ Backaches ❑ Cramps
❑ Sore Breasts ❑ Acne
❑ Cravings ❑ Other:_____

Sleep ☺ 😐 ☹
Energy ☺ 😐 ☹
Mood ☺ 😐 ☹

_____

_____

_____

DAY THREE OF CYCLE

❑ Backaches ❑ Cramps
❑ Sore Breasts ❑ Acne
❑ Cravings ❑ Other:_____

Sleep ☺ 😐 ☹
Energy ☺ 😐 ☹
Mood ☺ 😐 ☹

_____

_____

_____

Day Four of Cycle

❏ Backaches ❏ Cramps Sleep 🙂 😐 🙁
❏ Sore Breasts ❏ Acne Energy 🙂 😐 🙁
❏ Cravings ❏ Other:_____ Mood 🙂 😐 🙁

_____

_____

_____

Day Five of Cycle

❏ Backaches ❏ Cramps Sleep 🙂 😐 🙁
❏ Sore Breasts ❏ Acne Energy 🙂 😐 🙁
❏ Cravings ❏ Other:_____ Mood 🙂 😐 🙁

_____

_____

_____

Day six of Cycle

❏ Backaches ❏ Cramps Sleep 🙂 😐 🙁
❏ Sore Breasts ❏ Acne Energy 🙂 😐 🙁
❏ Cravings ❏ Other:_____ Mood 🙂 😐 🙁

_____

_____

_____

Day seven of Cycle

❏ Backaches ❏ Cramps Sleep 🙂 😐 🙁
❏ Sore Breasts ❏ Acne Energy 🙂 😐 🙁
❏ Cravings ❏ Other:_____ Mood 🙂 😐 🙁

_____

_____

_____

J	F	M	A	M	J	J	A	S	O	N	D

1	2	3	4	5	6	7	8	9	10	11	12
13	14	15	16	17	18	19	20	21	22	23	24
25	26	27	28	29	30	31	*Cross off dates that do not apply for this month				

KEY: ■ Heavy ◣ Medium △ Light • Spotting ⊠ N/A

_____ DAYS SINCE LAST PERIOD ☾ EXPECT NEXT PERIOD AROUND_____

DAY ONE OF CYCLE

❏ Backaches ❏ Cramps Sleep ☺ 😐 ☹
❏ Sore Breasts ❏ Acne Energy ☺ 😐 ☹
❏ Cravings ❏ Other:_____ Mood ☺ 😐 ☹

_____

_____

_____

DAY TWO OF CYCLE

❏ Backaches ❏ Cramps Sleep ☺ 😐 ☹
❏ Sore Breasts ❏ Acne Energy ☺ 😐 ☹
❏ Cravings ❏ Other:_____ Mood ☺ 😐 ☹

_____

_____

_____

DAY THREE OF CYCLE

❏ Backaches ❏ Cramps Sleep ☺ 😐 ☹
❏ Sore Breasts ❏ Acne Energy ☺ 😐 ☹
❏ Cravings ❏ Other:_____ Mood ☺ 😐 ☹

_____

_____

Day Four of Cycle

❑ Backaches   ❑ Cramps   Sleep ☺ 😐 ☹
❑ Sore Breasts   ❑ Acne   Energy ☺ 😐 ☹
❑ Cravings   ❑ Other:_____   Mood ☺ 😐 ☹

_____

_____

_____

Day Five of Cycle

❑ Backaches   ❑ Cramps   Sleep ☺ 😐 ☹
❑ Sore Breasts   ❑ Acne   Energy ☺ 😐 ☹
❑ Cravings   ❑ Other:_____   Mood ☺ 😐 ☹

_____

_____

_____

Day six of Cycle

❑ Backaches   ❑ Cramps   Sleep ☺ 😐 ☹
❑ Sore Breasts   ❑ Acne   Energy ☺ 😐 ☹
❑ Cravings   ❑ Other:_____   Mood ☺ 😐 ☹

_____

_____

_____

Day seven of Cycle

❑ Backaches   ❑ Cramps   Sleep ☺ 😐 ☹
❑ Sore Breasts   ❑ Acne   Energy ☺ 😐 ☹
❑ Cravings   ❑ Other:_____   Mood ☺ 😐 ☹

_____

_____

_____

| J | F | M | A | M | J | J | A | S | O | N | D |

1	2	3	4	5	6	7	8	9	10	11	12
13	14	15	16	17	18	19	20	21	22	23	24
25	26	27	28	29	30	31	*Cross off dates that do not apply for this month				

KEY: ■ Heavy ◣ Medium △ Light • Spotting ⊠ N/A

_____ DAYS SINCE LAST PERIOD ☾ EXPECT NEXT PERIOD AROUND_____

Day One of Cycle

❑ Backaches ❑ Cramps Sleep ☺ 😐 ☹
❑ Sore Breasts ❑ Acne Energy ☺ 😐 ☹
❑ Cravings ❑ Other:_____ Mood ☺ 😐 ☹

_____

_____

_____

Day two of Cycle

❑ Backaches ❑ Cramps Sleep ☺ 😐 ☹
❑ Sore Breasts ❑ Acne Energy ☺ 😐 ☹
❑ Cravings ❑ Other:_____ Mood ☺ 😐 ☹

_____

_____

_____

Day three of Cycle

❑ Backaches ❑ Cramps Sleep ☺ 😐 ☹
❑ Sore Breasts ❑ Acne Energy ☺ 😐 ☹
❑ Cravings ❑ Other:_____ Mood ☺ 😐 ☹

_____

_____

Year:_____

Day Four of Cycle

❏ Backaches ❏ Cramps
❏ Sore Breasts ❏ Acne
❏ Cravings ❏ Other:_____

Sleep ☺ 😐 ☹
Energy ☺ 😐 ☹
Mood ☺ 😐 ☹

_____

_____

_____

Day Five of Cycle

❏ Backaches ❏ Cramps
❏ Sore Breasts ❏ Acne
❏ Cravings ❏ Other:_____

Sleep ☺ 😐 ☹
Energy ☺ 😐 ☹
Mood ☺ 😐 ☹

_____

_____

_____

Day Six of Cycle

❏ Backaches ❏ Cramps
❏ Sore Breasts ❏ Acne
❏ Cravings ❏ Other:_____

Sleep ☺ 😐 ☹
Energy ☺ 😐 ☹
Mood ☺ 😐 ☹

_____

_____

_____

Day Seven of Cycle

❏ Backaches ❏ Cramps
❏ Sore Breasts ❏ Acne
❏ Cravings ❏ Other:_____

Sleep ☺ 😐 ☹
Energy ☺ 😐 ☹
Mood ☺ 😐 ☹

_____

_____

_____

| J | F | M | A | M | J | J | A | S | O | N | D |

1	2	3	4	5	6	7	8	9	10	11	12
13	14	15	16	17	18	19	20	21	22	23	24
25	26	27	28	29	30	31	*Cross off dates that do not apply for this month				

KEY: ■ Heavy ◣ Medium △ Light • Spotting ⊠ N/A

_____ DAYS SINCE LAST PERIOD ☾ EXPECT NEXT PERIOD AROUND_____

DAY ONE OF CYCLE

❏ Backaches ❏ Cramps
❏ Sore Breasts ❏ Acne
❏ Cravings ❏ Other:_____

Sleep ☺ 😐 ☹
Energy ☺ 😐 ☹
Mood ☺ 😐 ☹

_____
_____
_____

DAY TWO OF CYCLE

❏ Backaches ❏ Cramps
❏ Sore Breasts ❏ Acne
❏ Cravings ❏ Other:_____

Sleep ☺ 😐 ☹
Energy ☺ 😐 ☹
Mood ☺ 😐 ☹

_____
_____
_____

DAY THREE OF CYCLE

❏ Backaches ❏ Cramps
❏ Sore Breasts ❏ Acne
❏ Cravings ❏ Other:_____

Sleep ☺ 😐 ☹
Energy ☺ 😐 ☹
Mood ☺ 😐 ☹

_____
_____
_____

Year:_____

DAY FOUR OF CYCLE

❏ Backaches ❏ Cramps
❏ Sore Breasts ❏ Acne
❏ Cravings ❏ Other:_____

Sleep 🙂 😐 🙁
Energy 🙂 😐 🙁
Mood 🙂 😐 🙁

_____
_____
_____

DAY FIVE OF CYCLE

❏ Backaches ❏ Cramps
❏ Sore Breasts ❏ Acne
❏ Cravings ❏ Other:_____

Sleep 🙂 😐 🙁
Energy 🙂 😐 🙁
Mood 🙂 😐 🙁

_____
_____
_____

DAY SIX OF CYCLE

❏ Backaches ❏ Cramps
❏ Sore Breasts ❏ Acne
❏ Cravings ❏ Other:_____

Sleep 🙂 😐 🙁
Energy 🙂 😐 🙁
Mood 🙂 😐 🙁

_____
_____
_____

DAY SEVEN OF CYCLE

❏ Backaches ❏ Cramps
❏ Sore Breasts ❏ Acne
❏ Cravings ❏ Other:_____

Sleep 🙂 😐 🙁
Energy 🙂 😐 🙁
Mood 🙂 😐 🙁

_____
_____
_____

| J | F | M | A | M | J | J | A | S | O | N | D |

1	2	3	4	5	6	7	8	9	10	11	12
13	14	15	16	17	18	19	20	21	22	23	24
25	26	27	28	29	30	31	*Cross off dates that do not apply for this month				

KEY: ■ Heavy ◤ Medium △ Light • Spotting ⊠ N/A

_____ DAYS SINCE LAST PERIOD 🌙 EXPECT NEXT PERIOD AROUND_____

DAY ONE OF CYCLE

- ❏ Backaches
- ❏ Sore Breasts
- ❏ Cravings
- ❏ Cramps
- ❏ Acne
- ❏ Other:_____

Sleep ☺ 😐 ☹
Energy ☺ 😐 ☹
Mood ☺ 😐 ☹

_____

_____

_____

DAY TWO OF CYCLE

- ❏ Backaches
- ❏ Sore Breasts
- ❏ Cravings
- ❏ Cramps
- ❏ Acne
- ❏ Other:_____

Sleep ☺ 😐 ☹
Energy ☺ 😐 ☹
Mood ☺ 😐 ☹

_____

_____

_____

DAY THREE OF CYCLE

- ❏ Backaches
- ❏ Sore Breasts
- ❏ Cravings
- ❏ Cramps
- ❏ Acne
- ❏ Other:_____

Sleep ☺ 😐 ☹
Energy ☺ 😐 ☹
Mood ☺ 😐 ☹

_____

_____

_____

Year:_____

Day Four of Cycle

❏ Backaches ❏ Cramps
❏ Sore Breasts ❏ Acne
❏ Cravings ❏ Other:_____

Sleep ☺ 😐 ☹
Energy ☺ 😐 ☹
Mood ☺ 😐 ☹

_____

_____

_____

Day Five of Cycle

❏ Backaches ❏ Cramps
❏ Sore Breasts ❏ Acne
❏ Cravings ❏ Other:_____

Sleep ☺ 😐 ☹
Energy ☺ 😐 ☹
Mood ☺ 😐 ☹

_____

_____

_____

Day six of Cycle

❏ Backaches ❏ Cramps
❏ Sore Breasts ❏ Acne
❏ Cravings ❏ Other:_____

Sleep ☺ 😐 ☹
Energy ☺ 😐 ☹
Mood ☺ 😐 ☹

_____

_____

_____

Day seven of Cycle

❏ Backaches ❏ Cramps
❏ Sore Breasts ❏ Acne
❏ Cravings ❏ Other:_____

Sleep ☺ 😐 ☹
Energy ☺ 😐 ☹
Mood ☺ 😐 ☹

_____

_____

_____

| J | F | M | A | M | J | J | A | S | O | N | D |

1	2	3	4	5	6	7	8	9	10	11	12
13	14	15	16	17	18	19	20	21	22	23	24
25	26	27	28	29	30	31	*Cross off dates that do not apply for this month				

KEY: ■ Heavy ◣ Medium ◺ Light • Spotting ⊠ N/A

_____ DAYS SINCE LAST PERIOD 🌙 EXPECT NEXT PERIOD AROUND_____

Day One of Cycle

- ❑ Backaches
- ❑ Sore Breasts
- ❑ Cravings
- ❑ Cramps
- ❑ Acne
- ❑ Other:_____

Sleep ☺ 😐 ☹
Energy ☺ 😐 ☹
Mood ☺ 😐 ☹

_____

_____

_____

Day two of Cycle

- ❑ Backaches
- ❑ Sore Breasts
- ❑ Cravings
- ❑ Cramps
- ❑ Acne
- ❑ Other:_____

Sleep ☺ 😐 ☹
Energy ☺ 😐 ☹
Mood ☺ 😐 ☹

_____

_____

_____

Day three of Cycle

- ❑ Backaches
- ❑ Sore Breasts
- ❑ Cravings
- ❑ Cramps
- ❑ Acne
- ❑ Other:_____

Sleep ☺ 😐 ☹
Energy ☺ 😐 ☹
Mood ☺ 😐 ☹

_____

_____

Day Four of Cycle

❏ Backaches   ❏ Cramps   Sleep ☺ 😐 ☹
❏ Sore Breasts   ❏ Acne   Energy ☺ 😐 ☹
❏ Cravings   ❏ Other:_____   Mood ☺ 😐 ☹

_____

_____

_____

Day Five of Cycle

❏ Backaches   ❏ Cramps   Sleep ☺ 😐 ☹
❏ Sore Breasts   ❏ Acne   Energy ☺ 😐 ☹
❏ Cravings   ❏ Other:_____   Mood ☺ 😐 ☹

_____

_____

_____

Day six of Cycle

❏ Backaches   ❏ Cramps   Sleep ☺ 😐 ☹
❏ Sore Breasts   ❏ Acne   Energy ☺ 😐 ☹
❏ Cravings   ❏ Other:_____   Mood ☺ 😐 ☹

_____

_____

_____

Day seven of Cycle

❏ Backaches   ❏ Cramps   Sleep ☺ 😐 ☹
❏ Sore Breasts   ❏ Acne   Energy ☺ 😐 ☹
❏ Cravings   ❏ Other:_____   Mood ☺ 😐 ☹

_____

_____

_____

| J | F | M | A | M | J | J | A | S | O | N | D |

1	2	3	4	5	6	7	8	9	10	11	12
13	14	15	16	17	18	19	20	21	22	23	24
25	26	27	28	29	30	31	*Cross off dates that do not apply for this month				

KEY: ■ Heavy ◣ Medium △ Light • Spotting ⊠ N/A

_____ DAYS SINCE LAST PERIOD 🌙 EXPECT NEXT PERIOD AROUND_____

Day One of Cycle

❏ Backaches ❏ Cramps
❏ Sore Breasts ❏ Acne
❏ Cravings ❏ Other:_____

Sleep ☺ 😐 ☹
Energy ☺ 😐 ☹
Mood ☺ 😐 ☹

_____

_____

_____

Day two of Cycle

❏ Backaches ❏ Cramps
❏ Sore Breasts ❏ Acne
❏ Cravings ❏ Other:_____

Sleep ☺ 😐 ☹
Energy ☺ 😐 ☹
Mood ☺ 😐 ☹

_____

_____

_____

Day three of Cycle

❏ Backaches ❏ Cramps
❏ Sore Breasts ❏ Acne
❏ Cravings ❏ Other:_____

Sleep ☺ 😐 ☹
Energy ☺ 😐 ☹
Mood ☺ 😐 ☹

_____

_____

Day Four of Cycle

❏ Backaches ❏ Cramps
❏ Sore Breasts ❏ Acne
❏ Cravings ❏ Other:_____

Sleep ☺ 😐 ☹
Energy ☺ 😐 ☹
Mood ☺ 😐 ☹

_____

_____

_____

Day Five of Cycle

❏ Backaches ❏ Cramps
❏ Sore Breasts ❏ Acne
❏ Cravings ❏ Other:_____

Sleep ☺ 😐 ☹
Energy ☺ 😐 ☹
Mood ☺ 😐 ☹

_____

_____

_____

Day Six of Cycle

❏ Backaches ❏ Cramps
❏ Sore Breasts ❏ Acne
❏ Cravings ❏ Other:_____

Sleep ☺ 😐 ☹
Energy ☺ 😐 ☹
Mood ☺ 😐 ☹

_____

_____

_____

Day Seven of Cycle

❏ Backaches ❏ Cramps
❏ Sore Breasts ❏ Acne
❏ Cravings ❏ Other:_____

Sleep ☺ 😐 ☹
Energy ☺ 😐 ☹
Mood ☺ 😐 ☹

_____

_____

_____

J	F	M	A	M	J	J	A	S	O	N	D

1	2	3	4	5	6	7	8	9	10	11	12
13	14	15	16	17	18	19	20	21	22	23	24
25	26	27	28	29	30	31	*Cross off dates that do not apply for this month				

KEY: ■ Heavy ◣ Medium △ Light • Spotting ⊠ N/A

_____ DAYS SINCE LAST PERIOD 🌙 EXPECT NEXT PERIOD AROUND_____

DAY ONE OF CYCLE

❏ Backaches ❏ Cramps   Sleep ☺ 😐 ☹
❏ Sore Breasts ❏ Acne   Energy ☺ 😐 ☹
❏ Cravings ❏ Other:_____   Mood ☺ 😐 ☹

_____

_____

_____

DAY TWO OF CYCLE

❏ Backaches ❏ Cramps   Sleep ☺ 😐 ☹
❏ Sore Breasts ❏ Acne   Energy ☺ 😐 ☹
❏ Cravings ❏ Other:_____   Mood ☺ 😐 ☹

_____

_____

_____

DAY THREE OF CYCLE

❏ Backaches ❏ Cramps   Sleep ☺ 😐 ☹
❏ Sore Breasts ❏ Acne   Energy ☺ 😐 ☹
❏ Cravings ❏ Other:_____   Mood ☺ 😐 ☹

_____

_____

Day Four of Cycle

- ❏ Backaches
- ❏ Sore Breasts
- ❏ Cravings

- ❏ Cramps
- ❏ Acne
- ❏ Other:_____

Sleep ☺ 😐 ☹
Energy ☺ 😐 ☹
Mood ☺ 😐 ☹

_____

_____

_____

Day Five of Cycle

- ❏ Backaches
- ❏ Sore Breasts
- ❏ Cravings

- ❏ Cramps
- ❏ Acne
- ❏ Other:_____

Sleep ☺ 😐 ☹
Energy ☺ 😐 ☹
Mood ☺ 😐 ☹

_____

_____

_____

Day Six of Cycle

- ❏ Backaches
- ❏ Sore Breasts
- ❏ Cravings

- ❏ Cramps
- ❏ Acne
- ❏ Other:_____

Sleep ☺ 😐 ☹
Energy ☺ 😐 ☹
Mood ☺ 😐 ☹

_____

_____

_____

Day Seven of Cycle

- ❏ Backaches
- ❏ Sore Breasts
- ❏ Cravings

- ❏ Cramps
- ❏ Acne
- ❏ Other:_____

Sleep ☺ 😐 ☹
Energy ☺ 😐 ☹
Mood ☺ 😐 ☹

_____

_____

_____

| J | F | M | A | M | J | J | A | S | O | N | D |

1	2	3	4	5	6	7	8	9	10	11	12
13	14	15	16	17	18	19	20	21	22	23	24
25	26	27	28	29	30	31	*Cross off dates that do not apply for this month				

KEY: ■ Heavy ◨ Medium △ Light • Spotting ⊠ N/A

_____ DAYS SINCE LAST PERIOD   ☾   EXPECT NEXT PERIOD AROUND_____

Day One of Cycle

- ❏ Backaches
- ❏ Sore Breasts
- ❏ Cravings
- ❏ Cramps
- ❏ Acne
- ❏ Other:_____

Sleep ☺ 😐 ☹
Energy ☺ 😐 ☹
Mood ☺ 😐 ☹

_____

_____

Day two of Cycle

- ❏ Backaches
- ❏ Sore Breasts
- ❏ Cravings
- ❏ Cramps
- ❏ Acne
- ❏ Other:_____

Sleep ☺ 😐 ☹
Energy ☺ 😐 ☹
Mood ☺ 😐 ☹

_____

_____

Day three of Cycle

- ❏ Backaches
- ❏ Sore Breasts
- ❏ Cravings
- ❏ Cramps
- ❏ Acne
- ❏ Other:_____

Sleep ☺ 😐 ☹
Energy ☺ 😐 ☹
Mood ☺ 😐 ☹

_____

_____

Day Four of Cycle

❏ Backaches   ❏ Cramps   Sleep ☺ 😐 ☹
❏ Sore Breasts ❏ Acne   Energy ☺ 😐 ☹
❏ Cravings   ❏ Other:_____ Mood ☺ 😐 ☹

_____

_____

_____

Day Five of Cycle

❏ Backaches   ❏ Cramps   Sleep ☺ 😐 ☹
❏ Sore Breasts ❏ Acne   Energy ☺ 😐 ☹
❏ Cravings   ❏ Other:_____ Mood ☺ 😐 ☹

_____

_____

_____

Day Six of Cycle

❏ Backaches   ❏ Cramps   Sleep ☺ 😐 ☹
❏ Sore Breasts ❏ Acne   Energy ☺ 😐 ☹
❏ Cravings   ❏ Other:_____ Mood ☺ 😐 ☹

_____

_____

_____

Day Seven of Cycle

❏ Backaches   ❏ Cramps   Sleep ☺ 😐 ☹
❏ Sore Breasts ❏ Acne   Energy ☺ 😐 ☹
❏ Cravings   ❏ Other:_____ Mood ☺ 😐 ☹

_____

_____

_____

J	F	M	A	M	J	J	A	S	O	N	D

1	2	3	4	5	6	7	8	9	10	11	12
13	14	15	16	17	18	19	20	21	22	23	24
25	26	27	28	29	30	31	*Cross off dates that do not apply for this month				

KEY: ■ Heavy ◣ Medium △ Light • Spotting ⊠ N/A

_____ DAYS SINCE LAST PERIOD ☾ EXPECT NEXT PERIOD AROUND_____

DAY ONE OF CYCLE

- ❑ Backaches
- ❑ Sore Breasts
- ❑ Cravings
- ❑ Cramps
- ❑ Acne
- ❑ Other:_____

Sleep ☺ 😐 ☹
Energy ☺ 😐 ☹
Mood ☺ 😐 ☹

_____

_____

DAY TWO OF CYCLE

- ❑ Backaches
- ❑ Sore Breasts
- ❑ Cravings
- ❑ Cramps
- ❑ Acne
- ❑ Other:_____

Sleep ☺ 😐 ☹
Energy ☺ 😐 ☹
Mood ☺ 😐 ☹

_____

_____

DAY THREE OF CYCLE

- ❑ Backaches
- ❑ Sore Breasts
- ❑ Cravings
- ❑ Cramps
- ❑ Acne
- ❑ Other:_____

Sleep ☺ 😐 ☹
Energy ☺ 😐 ☹
Mood ☺ 😐 ☹

_____

_____

Year:_____

Day Four of Cycle

❏ Backaches ❏ Cramps
❏ Sore Breasts ❏ Acne
❏ Cravings ❏ Other:_____

Sleep 🙂 😐 🙁
Energy 🙂 😐 🙁
Mood 🙂 😐 🙁

_____

_____

_____

Day Five of Cycle

❏ Backaches ❏ Cramps
❏ Sore Breasts ❏ Acne
❏ Cravings ❏ Other:_____

Sleep 🙂 😐 🙁
Energy 🙂 😐 🙁
Mood 🙂 😐 🙁

_____

_____

_____

Day Six of Cycle

❏ Backaches ❏ Cramps
❏ Sore Breasts ❏ Acne
❏ Cravings ❏ Other:_____

Sleep 🙂 😐 🙁
Energy 🙂 😐 🙁
Mood 🙂 😐 🙁

_____

_____

_____

Day Seven of Cycle

❏ Backaches ❏ Cramps
❏ Sore Breasts ❏ Acne
❏ Cravings ❏ Other:_____

Sleep 🙂 😐 🙁
Energy 🙂 😐 🙁
Mood 🙂 😐 🙁

_____

_____

_____

| J | F | M | A | M | J | J | A | S | O | N | D |

1	2	3	4	5	6	7	8	9	10	11	12
13	14	15	16	17	18	19	20	21	22	23	24
25	26	27	28	29	30	31	*Cross off dates that do not apply for this month				

KEY: ■ Heavy ◣ Medium △ Light • Spotting ⊠ N/A

_____ DAYS SINCE LAST PERIOD ☾ EXPECT NEXT PERIOD AROUND_____

Day One of Cycle

❑ Backaches   ❑ Cramps   Sleep   ☺ 😐 ☹
❑ Sore Breasts ❑ Acne   Energy ☺ 😐 ☹
❑ Cravings   ❑ Other:_____   Mood   ☺ 😐 ☹

_____

_____

_____

Day two of Cycle

❑ Backaches   ❑ Cramps   Sleep   ☺ 😐 ☹
❑ Sore Breasts ❑ Acne   Energy ☺ 😐 ☹
❑ Cravings   ❑ Other:_____   Mood   ☺ 😐 ☹

_____

_____

_____

Day three of Cycle

❑ Backaches   ❑ Cramps   Sleep   ☺ 😐 ☹
❑ Sore Breasts ❑ Acne   Energy ☺ 😐 ☹
❑ Cravings   ❑ Other:_____   Mood   ☺ 😐 ☹

_____

_____

Day Four of Cycle

❑ Backaches ❑ Cramps Sleep 🙂 😐 🙁
❑ Sore Breasts ❑ Acne Energy 🙂 😐 🙁
❑ Cravings ❑ Other:_____ Mood 🙂 😐 🙁

_____

_____

_____

Day Five of Cycle

❑ Backaches ❑ Cramps Sleep 🙂 😐 🙁
❑ Sore Breasts ❑ Acne Energy 🙂 😐 🙁
❑ Cravings ❑ Other:_____ Mood 🙂 😐 🙁

_____

_____

_____

Day Six of Cycle

❑ Backaches ❑ Cramps Sleep 🙂 😐 🙁
❑ Sore Breasts ❑ Acne Energy 🙂 😐 🙁
❑ Cravings ❑ Other:_____ Mood 🙂 😐 🙁

_____

_____

_____

Day Seven of Cycle

❑ Backaches ❑ Cramps Sleep 🙂 😐 🙁
❑ Sore Breasts ❑ Acne Energy 🙂 😐 🙁
❑ Cravings ❑ Other:_____ Mood 🙂 😐 🙁

_____

_____

_____

| J | F | M | A | M | J | J | A | S | O | N | D |

1	2	3	4	5	6	7	8	9	10	11	12
13	14	15	16	17	18	19	20	21	22	23	24
25	26	27	28	29	30	31	*Cross off dates that do not apply for this month				

KEY: ■ Heavy ◣ Medium △ Light • Spotting ⊠ N/A

_____ DAYS SINCE LAST PERIOD   🌙   EXPECT NEXT PERIOD AROUND_____

Day One of Cycle

❏ Backaches ❏ Cramps Sleep ☺ 😐 ☹
❏ Sore Breasts ❏ Acne Energy ☺ 😐 ☹
❏ Cravings ❏ Other:_____ Mood ☺ 😐 ☹

_____

_____

Day two of Cycle

❏ Backaches ❏ Cramps Sleep ☺ 😐 ☹
❏ Sore Breasts ❏ Acne Energy ☺ 😐 ☹
❏ Cravings ❏ Other:_____ Mood ☺ 😐 ☹

_____

_____

Day three of Cycle

❏ Backaches ❏ Cramps Sleep ☺ 😐 ☹
❏ Sore Breasts ❏ Acne Energy ☺ 😐 ☹
❏ Cravings ❏ Other:_____ Mood ☺ 😐 ☹

_____

_____

Year:_____

Day Four of Cycle

- ❏ Backaches
- ❏ Sore Breasts
- ❏ Cravings
- ❏ Cramps
- ❏ Acne
- ❏ Other:_____

Sleep ☺ 😐 ☹
Energy ☺ 😐 ☹
Mood ☺ 😐 ☹

_____

_____

_____

Day Five of Cycle

- ❏ Backaches
- ❏ Sore Breasts
- ❏ Cravings
- ❏ Cramps
- ❏ Acne
- ❏ Other:_____

Sleep ☺ 😐 ☹
Energy ☺ 😐 ☹
Mood ☺ 😐 ☹

_____

_____

_____

Day Six of Cycle

- ❏ Backaches
- ❏ Sore Breasts
- ❏ Cravings
- ❏ Cramps
- ❏ Acne
- ❏ Other:_____

Sleep ☺ 😐 ☹
Energy ☺ 😐 ☹
Mood ☺ 😐 ☹

_____

_____

_____

Day Seven of Cycle

- ❏ Backaches
- ❏ Sore Breasts
- ❏ Cravings
- ❏ Cramps
- ❏ Acne
- ❏ Other:_____

Sleep ☺ 😐 ☹
Energy ☺ 😐 ☹
Mood ☺ 😐 ☹

_____

_____

_____

| J | F | M | A | M | J | J | A | S | O | N | D |

1	2	3	4	5	6	7	8	9	10	11	12
13	14	15	16	17	18	19	20	21	22	23	24
25	26	27	28	29	30	31	*Cross off dates that do not apply for this month				

KEY: ■ Heavy ◤ Medium △ Light • Spotting ⊠ N/A

_____ DAYS SINCE LAST PERIOD 🌙 EXPECT NEXT PERIOD AROUND_____

DAY ONE OF CYCLE

❏ Backaches   ❏ Cramps   Sleep ☺ 😐 ☹
❏ Sore Breasts ❏ Acne   Energy ☺ 😐 ☹
❏ Cravings   ❏ Other:_____ Mood   ☺ 😐 ☹

_____

_____

DAY TWO OF CYCLE

❏ Backaches   ❏ Cramps   Sleep ☺ 😐 ☹
❏ Sore Breasts ❏ Acne   Energy ☺ 😐 ☹
❏ Cravings   ❏ Other:_____ Mood   ☺ 😐 ☹

_____

_____

DAY THREE OF CYCLE

❏ Backaches   ❏ Cramps   Sleep ☺ 😐 ☹
❏ Sore Breasts ❏ Acne   Energy ☺ 😐 ☹
❏ Cravings   ❏ Other:_____ Mood   ☺ 😐 ☹

_____

_____

Day Four of Cycle

❏ Backaches ❏ Cramps   Sleep 🙂 😐 🙁
❏ Sore Breasts ❏ Acne   Energy 🙂 😐 🙁
❏ Cravings ❏ Other:_____   Mood 🙂 😐 🙁

_____

_____

_____

Day Five of Cycle

❏ Backaches ❏ Cramps   Sleep 🙂 😐 🙁
❏ Sore Breasts ❏ Acne   Energy 🙂 😐 🙁
❏ Cravings ❏ Other:_____   Mood 🙂 😐 🙁

_____

_____

_____

Day Six of Cycle

❏ Backaches ❏ Cramps   Sleep 🙂 😐 🙁
❏ Sore Breasts ❏ Acne   Energy 🙂 😐 🙁
❏ Cravings ❏ Other:_____   Mood 🙂 😐 🙁

_____

_____

_____

Day Seven of Cycle

❏ Backaches ❏ Cramps   Sleep 🙂 😐 🙁
❏ Sore Breasts ❏ Acne   Energy 🙂 😐 🙁
❏ Cravings ❏ Other:_____   Mood 🙂 😐 🙁

_____

_____

_____

| J | F | M | A | M | J | J | A | S | O | N | D |

1	2	3	4	5	6	7	8	9	10	11	12
13	14	15	16	17	18	19	20	21	22	23	24
25	26	27	28	29	30	31	*Cross off dates that do not apply for this month				

KEY: ■ Heavy ◣ Medium △ Light • Spotting ⊠ N/A

_____ DAYS SINCE LAST PERIOD 🌙 EXPECT NEXT PERIOD AROUND_____

DAY ONE OF CYCLE

❑ Backaches   ❑ Cramps   Sleep ☺ 😐 ☹
❑ Sore Breasts   ❑ Acne   Energy ☺ 😐 ☹
❑ Cravings   ❑ Other:_____   Mood ☺ 😐 ☹

_____

_____

DAY TWO OF CYCLE

❑ Backaches   ❑ Cramps   Sleep ☺ 😐 ☹
❑ Sore Breasts   ❑ Acne   Energy ☺ 😐 ☹
❑ Cravings   ❑ Other:_____   Mood ☺ 😐 ☹

_____

_____

DAY THREE OF CYCLE

❑ Backaches   ❑ Cramps   Sleep ☺ 😐 ☹
❑ Sore Breasts   ❑ Acne   Energy ☺ 😐 ☹
❑ Cravings   ❑ Other:_____   Mood ☺ 😐 ☹

_____

_____

Year:_____

Day Four of Cycle

❑ Backaches   ❑ Cramps   Sleep ☺ 😐 ☹
❑ Sore Breasts   ❑ Acne   Energy ☺ 😐 ☹
❑ Cravings   ❑ Other:_____   Mood ☺ 😐 ☹

_____

_____

_____

Day Five of Cycle

❑ Backaches   ❑ Cramps   Sleep ☺ 😐 ☹
❑ Sore Breasts   ❑ Acne   Energy ☺ 😐 ☹
❑ Cravings   ❑ Other:_____   Mood ☺ 😐 ☹

_____

_____

_____

Day Six of Cycle

❑ Backaches   ❑ Cramps   Sleep ☺ 😐 ☹
❑ Sore Breasts   ❑ Acne   Energy ☺ 😐 ☹
❑ Cravings   ❑ Other:_____   Mood ☺ 😐 ☹

_____

_____

_____

Day Seven of Cycle

❑ Backaches   ❑ Cramps   Sleep ☺ 😐 ☹
❑ Sore Breasts   ❑ Acne   Energy ☺ 😐 ☹
❑ Cravings   ❑ Other:_____   Mood ☺ 😐 ☹

_____

_____

_____

Order more unique journals and
notebooks made especially for
you by **Jasmin Brooke Creations**.
Available on Amazon.

Made in the USA
Columbia, SC
04 May 2022

59909874R00043